REVOLTING SCOTLAND

JEFF FALLOW

REVOLTING SCOTLAND

By

JEFF FALLOW

Luath Press Ltd.
Barr, Ayrshire KA26 9TN

First Edition 1992

DEDICATED TO
HUGH I. ORR
(1916 — 1990)

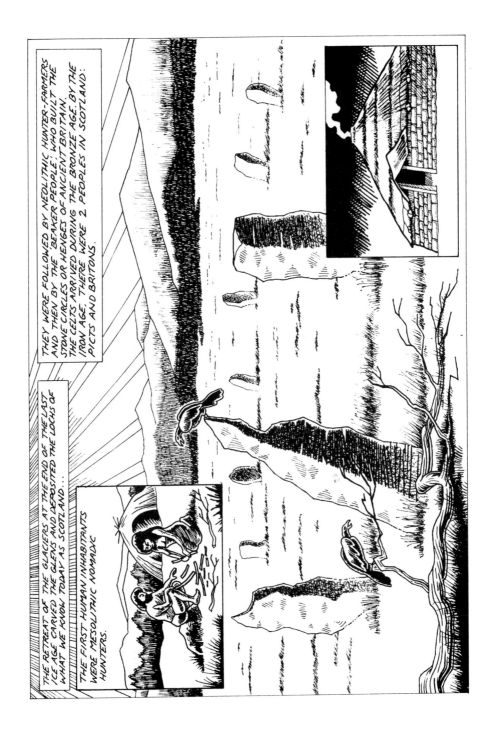

THE RETREAT OF THE GLACIERS AT THE END OF THE LAST ICE AGE CARVED THE GLENS AND DEPOSITED THE LOCHS OF WHAT WE KNOW TODAY AS SCOTLAND...

THE FIRST HUMAN INHABITANTS WERE MESOLITHIC NOMADIC HUNTERS.

THEY WERE FOLLOWED BY NEOLITHIC HUNTER-FARMERS AND THEN BY THE 'BEAKER PEOPLE', WHO BUILT THE STONE CIRCLES OR HENGES OF ANCIENT BRITAIN. THE CELTS ARRIVED DURING THE BRONZE AGE. BY THE IRON AGE, THERE WERE 2 PEOPLES IN SCOTLAND: PICTS AND BRITONS.

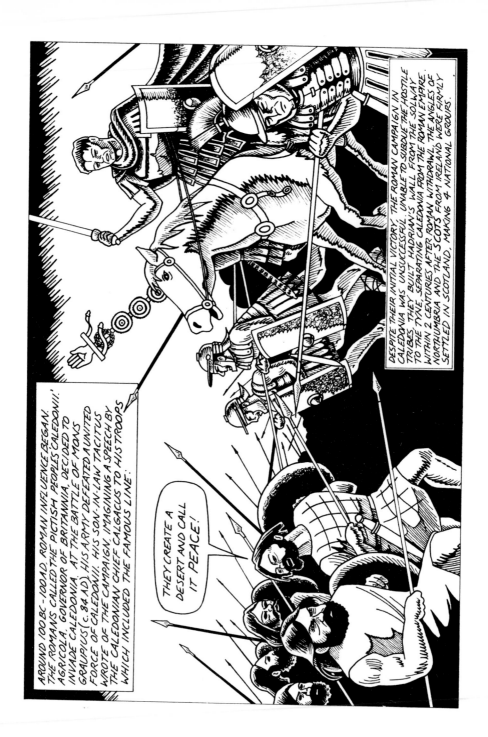

AROUND 100 B.C.- 100 A.D. ROMAN INFLUENCE BEGAN. THE ROMANS CALLED THE PICTISH PEOPLES CALEDONII. AGRICOLA, GOVERNOR OF BRITANNIA, DECIDED TO INVADE CALEDONIA. AT THE BATTLE OF MONS GRAUPIUS (c. 84 A.D.) HIS ARMY DEFEATED A UNITED FORCE OF CALEDONII. HIS SON-IN-LAW TACITUS WROTE OF THE CAMPAIGN, IMAGINING A SPEECH BY THE CALEDONIAN CHIEF CALGACUS TO HIS TROOPS WHICH INCLUDED THE FAMOUS LINE:

THEY CREATE A DESERT AND CALL IT PEACE!

DESPITE THEIR INITIAL VICTORY, THE ROMAN CAMPAIGN IN CALEDONIA WAS UNSUCCESSFUL. UNABLE TO SUBDUE THE HOSTILE TRIBES, THEY BUILT HADRIAN'S WALL FROM THE SOLWAY TO THE TYNE, SEPARATING CALEDONIA FROM THE ROMAN EMPIRE. WITHIN 2 CENTURIES AFTER ROMAN WITHDRAWL, THE ANGLES OF NORTHUMBRIA AND THE SCOTS FROM IRELAND WERE FIRMLY SETTLED IN SCOTLAND, MAKING 4 NATIONAL GROUPS.

-8-

ROMAN INFLUENCE LEFT CERTAIN CULTURAL LINKS ON THE PEOPLES OF SCOTLAND. EVEN MORE INFLUENTIAL WAS THE ADOPTION OF CHRISTIANITY AS THE NEW RELIGION OF THE 4 ETHNIC GROUPS.

SCOTS

PICTS

BRITONS

ANGLES

TYPICALLY, HOWEVER, POLITICAL UNITY WAS ACHIEVED BY MILITARY MEANS. IN 843 A.D., KENNETH MACALPIN, KING OF SCOTS, CONQUERED PICTLAND.

IN TIME, THE OTHER TERRITORIES WERE TAKEN OVER, FORMING A SINGLE KINGDOM OF SCOTLAND WITH A COMMON ETHNIC IDENTITY.

THEN, AS SCOTLAND EXTENDED ITS RULE SOUTHWARD AND ENGLAND NORTHWARD, BORDER DISPUTES AROSE. BUT A SCOTTISH DEFEAT REPEATEDLY MEANT THE SCOTTISH KINGS HAVING TO PAY HOMAGE TO ENGLAND.

I THINK IT'S TIME THESE SCOTS WERE PUT IN THEIR PLACE ONCE AND FOR ALL.

IN 1292, ENGLAND'S EDWARD I, 'HAMMER OF THE SCOTS', HAD PLANS TO CAPTURE AND SUBDUE THE WHOLE OF SCOTLAND.

EDWARD, HAVING BRUTALLY CONQUERED WALES, NOW PLANNED TO DO THE SAME WITH SCOTLAND. USING 'FIRE AND SWORD', HIS ARMIES INVADED AND PLUNDERED, MAKING SCOTLAND A SUBSERVIENT VASSAL STATE OF ENGLAND.

EDWARD HAD ALREADY USED DIPLOMACY TO MAKE JOHN BALLIOL, KING OF SCOTLAND, A PUPPET KING.

WHEN BALLIOL LATER REJECTED EDWARD'S DEMANDS, HE WAS FORCED INTO EXILE, RELINQUISHING HIS CROWN.

EDWARD NOW INTENDED TO ABOLISH SCOTTISH NATIONHOOD, RULING DIRECTLY FROM ENGLAND.

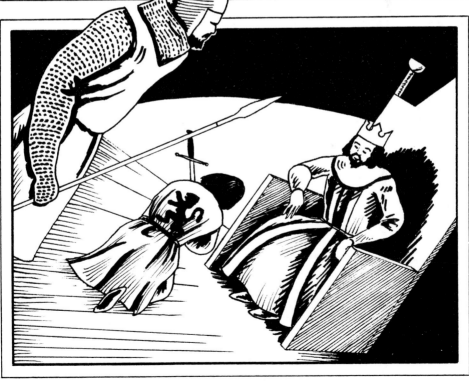

EDWARD INTENDED TO HUMILIATE AS WELL AS SUBDUE SCOTLAND. THE 'STONE OF DESTINY,' SCOTLAND'S CEREMONIAL CORONATION STONE, WAS STOLEN BY HIS TROOPS.

IT WAS PLACED BENEATH THE ENGLISH THRONE IN WESTMINSTER ABBEY.

IT REMAINS THERE TO THIS DAY.

IRONICALLY, EDWARD DID MORE TO HARDEN SCOTTISH NATIONAL FEELING THAN TO HUMILIATE.

SIR WILLIAM WALLACE, A LANARKSHIRE KNIGHT AND PATRIOT, LED A POPULAR UPRISING AGAINST THE OCCUPYING ENGLISH FORCES.

AT THE BATTLE OF STIRLING BRIDGE (1297), THE SCOTS DEFEATED THE ENGLISH IN THE FIRST MAJOR BATTLE OF THE WAR OF INDEPENDENCE.

WALLACE'S FORCE WAS ESSENTIALLY A POPULAR ARMY

WITH LITTLE HELP FROM THE SCOTTISH NOBILITY.

BUT EDWARD ONCE AGAIN DEFEATED AND SUPPRESSED THE SCOTTISH UPRISING.

WALLACE, BETRAYED BY A SCOTTISH KNIGHT, WAS CAPTURED AND TAKEN TO WESTMINSTER TO BE TRIED FOR TREASON.

EDWARD I DIED, LEAVING HIS THRONE TO HIS SON, EDWARD II, WHO WAS LESS COMPETENT THAN HIS FATHER.

AFTER THAT, BRUCE'S TASK OF RECLAIMING SCOTLAND BECAME EASIER.

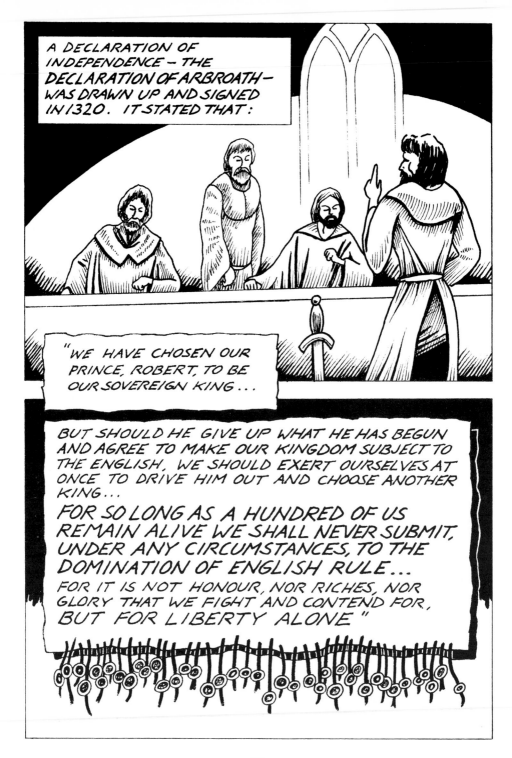

A DECLARATION OF INDEPENDENCE — THE DECLARATION OF ARBROATH — WAS DRAWN UP AND SIGNED IN 1320. IT STATED THAT:

"WE HAVE CHOSEN OUR PRINCE, ROBERT, TO BE OUR SOVEREIGN KING...

BUT SHOULD HE GIVE UP WHAT HE HAS BEGUN AND AGREE TO MAKE OUR KINGDOM SUBJECT TO THE ENGLISH, WE SHOULD EXERT OURSELVES AT ONCE TO DRIVE HIM OUT AND CHOOSE ANOTHER KING...

FOR SO LONG AS A HUNDRED OF US REMAIN ALIVE WE SHALL NEVER SUBMIT, UNDER ANY CIRCUMSTANCES, TO THE DOMINATION OF ENGLISH RULE...

FOR IT IS NOT HONOUR, NOR RICHES, NOR GLORY THAT WE FIGHT AND CONTEND FOR, BUT FOR LIBERTY ALONE"

SCOTLAND'S INDEPENDENCE WAS ESTABLISHED AND INTERNATIONALLY RECOGNISED, BUT BORDER WARFARE CONTINUED.

MANY ENGLISH ATTEMPTS WERE MADE TO CAPTURE THE BORDER LANDS — AN IMPORTANT SOURCE OF WEALTH.

ENGLAND'S EDWARD III INVADED AND OCCUPIED THE SOUTHERN COUNTIES FOR A TIME, UNTIL DEFENCE AND MAINTENANCE COSTS FORCED HIM TO ABANDON THEM.

-24-

MARY'S SON JAMES BECAME KING JAMES VI OF SCOTLAND.

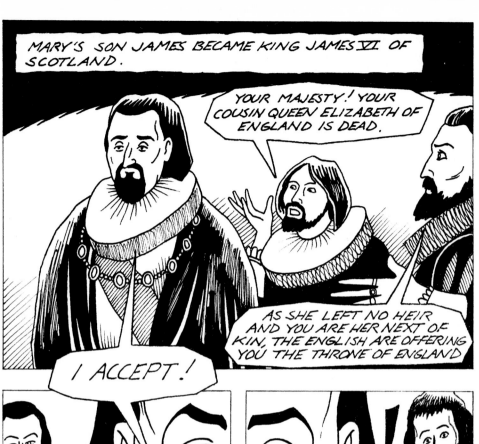

YOUR MAJESTY! YOUR COUSIN QUEEN ELIZABETH OF ENGLAND IS DEAD.

AS SHE LEFT NO HEIR AND YOU ARE HER NEXT OF KIN, THE ENGLISH ARE OFFERING YOU THE THRONE OF ENGLAND

I ACCEPT!

FROM NOW ON, SCOTLAND AND ENGLAND WILL RETAIN SEPARATE PARLIAMENTS UNDER A SINGLE CROWN...

BUT I WILL MOVE MY COURT TO LONDON AND I WILL RULE FROM THERE!

UNION OF CROWNS: 1603

-25-

JAMES FOUND LONDON WARMER AND WEALTHIER.

SO YOU MIGHT SAY HE WAS THE FIRST SCOT TO MOVE SOUTH TO FIND WORK?

AYE, ONE OF THE FIRST SCOTS TO 'MAKE GOOD' ABROAD WE ALWAYS HEAR ABOUT.

SCOTLAND STILL HAD A PARLIAMENT IN EDINBURGH BUT, SINCE ITS' DUTY WAS TO EXECUTE CROWN AUTHORITY, SCOTLAND WAS IN EFFECT RULED FROM LONDON. JAMES HIMSELF SAID HE HOPED SCOTLAND WOULD...

WITH TIME BECOME AS CUMBERLAND AND NORTHUMBERLAND AND THOSE OTHER REMOTE AND DISTANT SHIRES.

SCOTLAND LOST ITS' DIPLOMATIC AND ECONOMIC POWER.

JAMES' SON, CHARLES I, TRIED TO ABSORB THE SCOTTISH CHURCH INTO THE ANGLICAN TRADITION. THIS WAS RESISTED IN SCOTLAND BY THE 'COVENANTERS'. MEANWHILE, THE ENGLISH CIVIL WAR BROKE OUT BETWEEN...

MONARCHISTS (CAVALIERS)   AND   PARLIAMENTARIANS (ROUNDHEADS)

WE SUPPORT THE KING!

WE SUPPORT THE 'COMMONWEALTH'—A REPUBLIC WITH AN ELECTED PARLIAMENT!

THE SCOTTISH COVENANTERS SUPPORTED THE PARLIAMENTARIANS

BUT WHEN THE PARLIAMENTARIANS WON...

SCOTTISH TAXES

THEIR LEADER, OLIVER CROMWELL, IMPOSED RULE ON SCOTLAND. HIS RULE WAS STRICT AND SCOTLAND WAS TAXED HEAVILY FOR THE SHORT-LIVED UNION. CROMWELL BECAME 'LORD PROTECTOR'— A MILITARY DICTATOR.

THE RESTORATION OF THE MONARCHY IN 1660 ENDED CROMWELL'S UNION, GIVING SCOTLAND BACK ITS' 'INDEPENDENT' EDINBURGH PARLIAMENT (UNDER THE CROWN IN LONDON, OF COURSE).

IN 1691, WILLIAM III PASSED A LAW DESIGNED TO STAMP OUT SUSPECTED JACOBITES (SUPPORTERS OF JAMES VII, PRETENDER TO THE THRONE)...

ALL HIGHLAND CHIEFS MUST SWEAR LOYALTY TO ME!

THEY HAVE UNTIL THE 1st OF JANUARY 1692 TO GIVE OATH.

THE CHIEF OF THE MACDONALDS OF GLENCOE TURNED UP ON THE LAST DAY.

YOU'RE TOO LATE, MACDONALD

BUT I HAVE UNTIL TOMORROW!

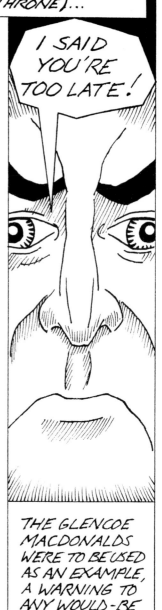

I SAID YOU'RE TOO LATE!

THE GLENCOE MACDONALDS WERE TO BE USED AS AN EXAMPLE, A WARNING TO ANY WOULD-BE DISLOYAL HIGHLANDERS.

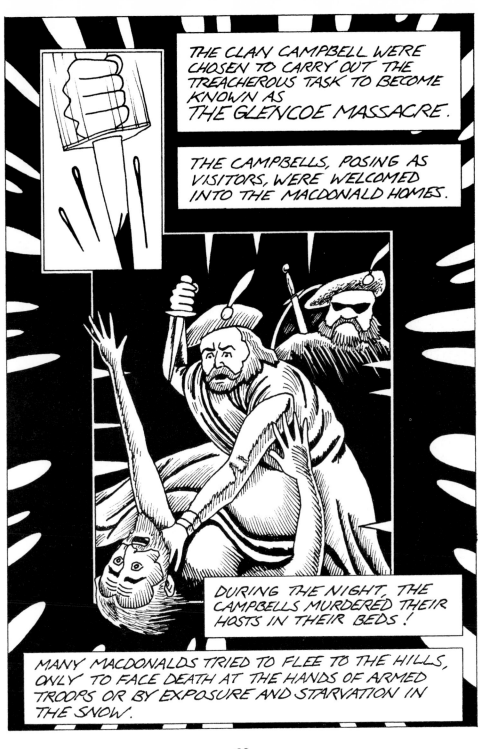

THE CLAN CAMPBELL WERE CHOSEN TO CARRY OUT THE TREACHEROUS TASK TO BECOME KNOWN AS THE GLENCOE MASSACRE.

THE CAMPBELLS, POSING AS VISITORS, WERE WELCOMED INTO THE MACDONALD HOMES.

DURING THE NIGHT, THE CAMPBELLS MURDERED THEIR HOSTS IN THEIR BEDS!

MANY MACDONALDS TRIED TO FLEE TO THE HILLS, ONLY TO FACE DEATH AT THE HANDS OF ARMED TROOPS OR BY EXPOSURE AND STARVATION IN THE SNOW.

BY NOW, COLONISATION OF THE AMERICAS HAD OPENED UP TRADE, MAKING COMMERCIAL TRADING MORE PROFITABLE THAN AGRICULTURE. WHILE THE RICH TURNED TO INVESTMENT IN TRADE, THE POOR COULD CHOOSE EMIGRATION TO ESCAPE UNEMPLOYMENT, DESTITUTION AND STARVATION. A SCOTTISH COLONY WAS ESTABLISHED AT DARIEN, PANAMA, IN HOPE TO BRING MONEY INTO SCOTLAND.

THE SCOTS SETTLERS WERE KILLED OFF BY DISEASE OR CHASED OUT BY SPANISH TROOPS.

YOUR MAJESTY! THE SCOTS ARE ASKING THE ENGLISH COLONIES FOR HELP.

NO! I DON'T WANT TO ANGER THE SPANISH. THEY MIGHT SIDE WITH OUR FRENCH RIVALS AGAINST ME.

TYPICAL! FAVOURING THE ENGLISH AND DISREGARDING THE SCOTS!

I WOULDN'T LIKE TO SEE A RISE OF JACOBITISM. MAYBE THERE SHOULD BE A UNION OF THE TWO PARLIAMENTS?

THE UNION OF PARLIAMENTS (1707)

WOULD BE ACHIEVED UNDER WILLIAM'S SUCCESSOR, QUEEN ANNE. THE ENGLISH PARLIAMENT CONSIDERED...

DO WE REALLY WANT TO ADOPT THE SCOTS, WITH ALL THEIR WRETCHED POVERTY?

WELL, THEY MIGHT POSE LESS OF A RIVAL OR THREAT. BESIDES, THEY WOULD BE A SOURCE OF TAX AND REVENUE.

THE MAJORITY OF SCOTS HAD NO SAY IN THE MATTER, THOUGH PROTEST WAS VOICED IN THE FORM OF PETITIONS TO THE SCOTTISH PARLIAMENT. THEY WERE IGNORED. PROTEST RIOTS AGAINST THE UNION BROKE OUT IN GLASGOW AND EDINBURGH, ONLY TO BE SUPPRESSED.

SCOTLAND WAS UNDER-REPRESENTED IN PARLIAMENT—
45 MPs AND 16 PEERS AMONG 500 ENGLISH DELEGATES.
HOWEVER, THERE REMAINED JACOBITE SUPPORT, IN ENGLAND
AS WELL AS SCOTLAND, BUT MOST STRONGLY IN THE
HIGHLANDS, WHICH HAD ITS OWN CULTURE, LANGUAGE
AND SOCIETY.

A RESTORATION OF THE STUART
MONARCHY, IT WAS HELD, WOULD
DISSOLVE THE UNION OF
PARLIAMENTS AND GUARANTEE
SCOTTISH RIGHTS.

THE JACOBITE PRETENDER JAMES VIII (& III) RETURNED FROM EXILE IN AN ATTEMPTED UPRISING IN 1715. IT FAILED AND HE FLED, BUT HIS SON CHARLES EDWARD STUART ('BONNIE PRINCE CHARLIE') TRIED AGAIN IN 1745...

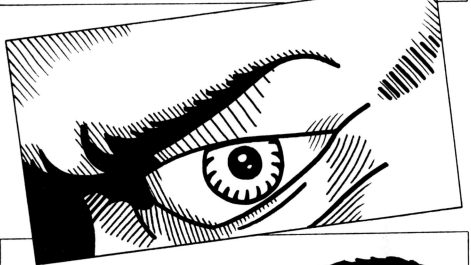

AT FIRST THE '45 REBELLION WAS SUCCESSFUL.

THE JACOBITES, ADVANCING FROM SCOTLAND, REACHED AS FAR SOUTH AS DERBY.

GRADUALLY THE CAMPAIGN FELL, THE REBELS WITHDRAWING TO THE HIGHLANDS.

THEN CAME THE FINAL BLOW:

CHARLES EDWARD STUART

16th APRIL 1746: THE BATTLE OF CULLODEN. THE LAST MILITARY BATTLE TO BE FOUGHT ON NATIVE BRITISH SOIL.

IT WAS A SLAUGHTER. 1200 HIGHLANDERS DIED, AS AGAINST 364 GOVERNMENT REDCOATS WITH THEIR SUPERIOR MILITARY TECHNOLOGY.

AFTERWARDS, GOVERNMENT COMMANDER WILLIAM AUGUSTUS, DUKE OF CUMBERLAND (KNOWN AS 'BUTCHER' CUMBERLAND) SHOWED NO MERCY TO PRISONERS AND WOUNDED, CONDONING WICKED ATROCITIES.

CHARLES FLED TO FRANCE AND THE HIGHLAND WAY OF LIFE ENDED FOREVER.

THE SPEAKING OF GAELIC AND THE WEARING OF TARTAN WERE BANNED FOR A DECADE

"WHEN THE NIGHT CAME, SILENT THEY LAY, DEAD ON CULLODEN'S FIELD".

AS JOHN MACLEAN LATER PUT IT:

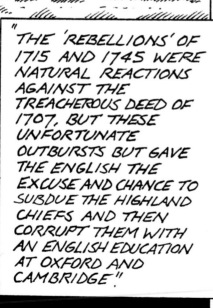

"THE 'REBELLIONS' OF 1715 AND 1745 WERE NATURAL REACTIONS AGAINST THE TREACHEROUS DEED OF 1707, BUT THESE UNFORTUNATE OUTBURSTS BUT GAVE THE ENGLISH THE EXCUSE AND CHANCE TO SUBDUE THE HIGHLAND CHIEFS AND THEN CORRUPT THEM WITH AN ENGLISH EDUCATION AT OXFORD AND CAMBRIDGE."

INFLUENCED BY THE FRENCH REVOLUTION, HIS WORKS SHOW A SYMPATHY FOR THE ORDINARY PEOPLE, SATIRIZING THE RULING CLASS AND LAMPOONING THE ESTABLISHMENT AND CONVENTIONAL MORALITY.

HIS SONG 'SCOTS WHA HAE', COMMEMORATING BANNOCKBURN AND WRITTEN IN PROTEST OVER THE TRANSPORTATION OF THE RADICAL ACTIVIST THOMAS MUIR, WAS BANNED AS SEDITIOUS.

SENTIMENT TOWARDS THE JACOBITES WAS EXPRESSED IN CERTAIN OF THE WORKS OF ROBERT BURNS (1759-1796) SCOTLAND'S GREAT RADICAL POET OF THE 18TH CENTURY.

ALTHOUGH OFTEN MISUNDERSTOOD, BURNS IS KNOWN TO HAVE HAD REPUBLICAN, NATIONALISTIC (i.e. ANTI-IMPERIALIST) SYMPATHIES, SIMULTANEOUSLY SUPPORTING SCOTTISH HOMERULE AND INTERNATIONAL FRATERNITY.

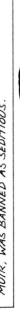

THE LATE 18th CENTURY SAW ANOTHER SEVERE BLOW TO THE SCOTTISH PEOPLE AND IDENTITY:
THE HIGHLAND CLEARANCES

HIGHLAND LANDOWNERS
REALISED THAT WOOL WAS
MUCH MORE PROFITABLE
THAN AGRICULTURE.
SHEEP-REARING WAS
INTRODUCED AND TENANTS
EVICTED. A SINGLE SHEPHERD
COULD WORK AN AREA
SUPPORTING 9 FAMILIES.
WHEN THE HIGHLANDERS
REBELLED AGAINST THIS
INVASION, THE MILITARY
WERE ALERTED AND THE
RINGLEADERS SENTENCED
TO TRANSPORTATION.

IN DUE COURSE, THE HIGHLANDS WERE
CLEARED OF MOST OF THE POPULATION.

THOUSANDS OF FAMILIES WERE DRIVEN OFF THEIR LAND, THEIR HOMES AND CROPS BURNED, FORCED TO MIGRATE

THEY GATHERED ON THE SHORE IN MULTITUDES, TO BE SHIPPED LIKE CATTLE TO CANADA, AMERICA, ETC.

OTHERS FLED TO GLASGOW

THE TRADITION OF SCOTS BEING FORCED TO LEAVE HOME FOR ECONOMIC REASONS CONTINUES TO THE PRESENT DAY

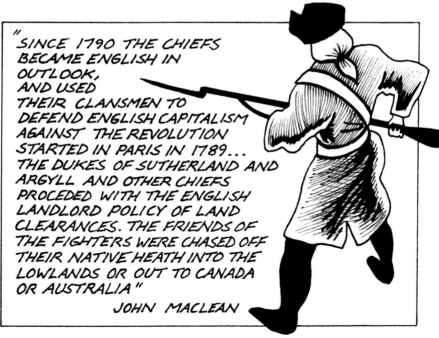

"SINCE 1790 THE CHIEFS BECAME ENGLISH IN OUTLOOK, AND USED THEIR CLANSMEN TO DEFEND ENGLISH CAPITALISM AGAINST THE REVOLUTION STARTED IN PARIS IN 1789... THE DUKES OF SUTHERLAND AND ARGYLL AND OTHER CHIEFS PROCEDED WITH THE ENGLISH LANDLORD POLICY OF LAND CLEARANCES. THE FRIENDS OF THE FIGHTERS WERE CHASED OFF THEIR NATIVE HEATH INTO THE LOWLANDS OR OUT TO CANADA OR AUSTRALIA"

JOHN MACLEAN

BY NOW, THE **INDUSTRIAL REVOLUTION** WAS GETTING UNDER WAY. AS TRADE AND INDUSTRY REPLACED SMALL FARMING AND COTTAGE WEAVING AS A PROFITABLE MEANS OF INCOME, FACTORY TOWNS AND LARGE FARMS GREW AS POOR WEAVERS AND EVICTED FARMERS FLOCKED TO THE TOWNS, MINES, DOCKS AND FACTORIES, FORMING THE SCOTTISH WORKING CLASS.

FACTORY OWNERS COULD AFFORD MORE PRODUCTIVE, MECHANISED METHODS

HANDCRAFT WORKERS COULD NOT COMPETE

THE INDUSTRIAL SLUMS SWELLED WITH DISPOSSESSED HIGHLANDERS AND UNEMPLOYED LOWLANDERS

THROUGHOUT THE 18th CENTURY, WORKING PEOPLE FORMED THE FIRST TRADE UNIONS (OR 'COMBINATIONS', AS THEY WERE THEN CALLED).

THEY ALSO FORMED COOPERATIVE SOCIETIES AND FRIENDLY SOCIETIES, WHICH SECURED A BASIC WELFARE FOR MEMBERS.

OVERMANNING IN GLASGOW COTTON MILLS BROUGHT ABOUT WAGE REDUCTIONS. IN 1787, WEAVERS MET ON GLASGOW GREEN AND WENT ON STRIKE. EMPLOYERS HAD TROOPS BREAK UP THE STRIKE. SIX WEAVERS WERE SHOT. RADICALISM CONTINUED TO SPREAD.

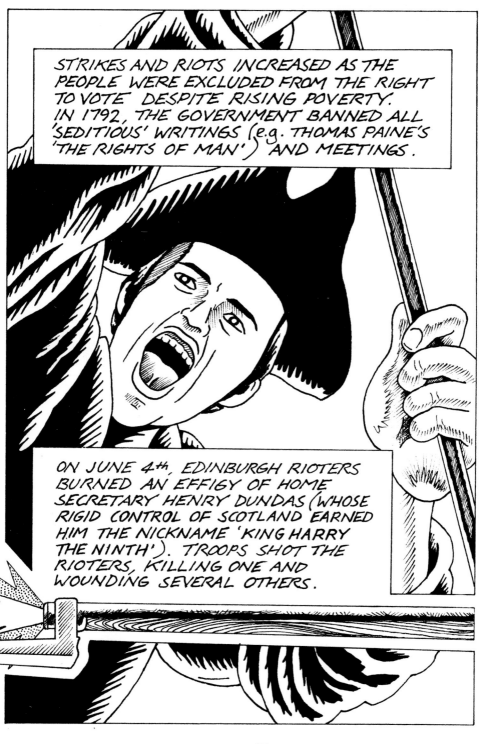

STRIKES AND RIOTS INCREASED AS THE PEOPLE WERE EXCLUDED FROM THE RIGHT TO VOTE DESPITE RISING POVERTY. IN 1792, THE GOVERNMENT BANNED ALL 'SEDITIOUS' WRITINGS (e.g. THOMAS PAINE'S 'THE RIGHTS OF MAN') AND MEETINGS.

ON JUNE 4th, EDINBURGH RIOTERS BURNED AN EFFIGY OF HOME SECRETARY HENRY DUNDAS (WHOSE RIGID CONTROL OF SCOTLAND EARNED HIM THE NICKNAME 'KING HARRY THE NINTH'). TROOPS SHOT THE RIOTERS, KILLING ONE AND WOUNDING SEVERAL OTHERS.

THAT SAME YEAR, THE 'FRIENDS OF THE PEOPLE' WAS FORMED, ORGANISING WIDELY IN LOWLAND TOWNS AND VILLAGES, ATTRACTING ALL KINDS OF WORKING PEOPLE INTO THE RANKS (THOUGH IT WAS MAINLY LED BY PROFESSIONAL AND MIDDLE CLASS INTELLECTUALS). AMONG THE LEADERS WERE:

THOMAS MUIR

WE SEEK DEMOCRATIC REFORM

WILLIAM SKIRVING

THOMAS FYSHE PALMER

OUR AIMS ARE MODERATE AND CONSTITUTIONAL

BUT THE GOVERNMENT AND RULING CLASS SEE US AS SUBVERSIVE

THOMAS MUIR, A YOUNG GLASGOW LAWYER, HAD BEEN IN CONTACT WITH THE 'UNITED IRISHMEN', A POLITICAL REFORM (LATER REPUBLICAN NATIONALIST) GROUP IN DUBLIN LED BY THEOBALD WOLFE TONE, FROM WHOM MUIR TOOK ADVICE.

WE MUST ACT OPENLY, ACTIVELY AND URGENTLY!

LET US TAKE AN OATH: 'TO LIVE FREE OR DIE!'

THE GOVERNMENT PANICKED...

INSURRECTION! REVOLUTION!!

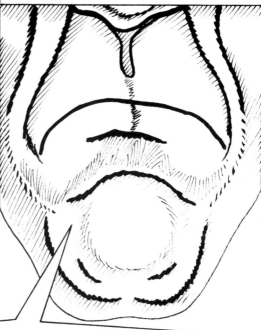

MUIR WAS ARRESTED, THEN TRIED IN EDINBURGH THE FOLLOWING YEAR BY THE NOTORIOUS JUDGE BRAXFIELD, WHO IGNORED 21 DEFENCE WITNESSES.

TRANSPORTATION TO AUSTRALIA! 14 YEARS!

ALSO SENTENCED WERE PALMER, SKIRVING AND TWO LONDON SYMPATHIZERS, MAURICE MARGAROT AND JOSEPH GERRALD.

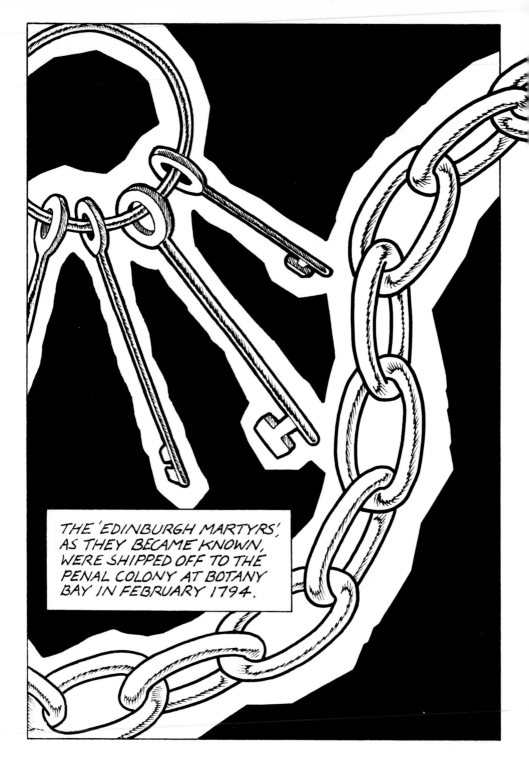

THE 'EDINBURGH MARTYRS,' AS THEY BECAME KNOWN, WERE SHIPPED OFF TO THE PENAL COLONY AT BOTANY BAY IN FEBRUARY 1794.

MUIR EVENTUALLY ESCAPED (WITH AMERICAN AND SPANISH HELP) TO FRANCE, WHERE HE WAS GREETED AS A HERO AND GIVEN POLITICAL ASYLUM AND HONORARY CITIZENSHIP.

-52-

THIS CONSPIRACY BECAME KNOWN AS **THE 'PIKE PLOT.'**

THE PLOT'S LEADERS, ROBERT WATT AND DAVID DOWNIE, WERE TRIED FOR HIGH TREASON.

WATT WAS HANGED AND BEHEADED

DOWNIE WAS TRANSPORTED

1797: GOVERNMENT PASSED THE MILITIA ACT:

WE'LL INTRODUCE COMPULSORY CONSCRIPTION...

INTO PART-TIME MILITARY SERVICE...

TO KEEP THE RABBLE IN THEIR PLACE!

WHAT ABOUT WE UPPER CLASSES? WON'T WE BE CONSCRIPTED TOO?

NOT NECESSARILY.

THE RICH CAN HIRE SUBSTITUTES TO TAKE THEIR PLACE!

THIS AROUSED ANGER AND WIDESPREAD RIOTING IN SCOTLAND. A PARTICULARLY SERIOUS RIOT OCCURRED AT TRANENT, EAST LOTHIAN, WHERE MINERS REFUSED TO BE CALLED UP....

CAVALRY CRUSHED THE RIOT, KILLING 12 PEOPLE INCLUDING A WOMAN AND A 13 YEAR OLD BOY.

LIKE THE 'UNITED IRISHMEN', THE UNITED SCOTSMEN' BEGAN AS A PARLIAMENTARY REFORM GROUP, LATER BECOMING REVOLUTIONARY.

FROM THE REMNANTS OF THE 'FRIENDS OF THE PEOPLE' EMERGED THE MORE MILITANT 'UNITED SCOTSMEN'.

LIKE THE 'FRIENDS OF THE PEOPLE', IT ADVOCATED SCOTTISH HOME RULE, UNIVERSAL SUFFRAGE AND ALSO ANNUAL GENERAL ELECTIONS, BUT ORGANISED SECRETLY.

'UNITED SCOTSMEN' LEADER **GEORGE MEALMAKER,** A DUNDEE HANDLOOM WEAVER, HAD BEEN AN ACTIVIST IN THE 'FRIENDS OF THE PEOPLE'.

HE HAD WRITTEN A MANIFESTO FOR THOMAS FYSHE PALMER, ONE OF THE TRANSPORTED MARTYRS.

MEALMAKER WAS CONVICTED OF SEDITION IN 1798.

LIKE HIS PREDECESSOR THOMAS MUIR, HE WAS SENTENCED TO 14 YEARS' TRANSPORTATION.

THE RISING TIDE OF 'SEDITION' CAUSED CONCERN AMONG THE UPPER ECHELONS OF SOCIETY. SCOTTISH JACOBITISM HAD BEEN BAD ENOUGH, BUT POPULAR SCOTTISH REPUBLICANISM POSED AN EVEN GREATER THREAT TO THE EXISTING ORDER. MANY SCOTS HAD PARTICIPATED IN BOTH THE AMERICAN AND FRENCH REVOLUTIONS AND THE SEEDS OF REBELLION WERE BEING CARRIED HOME.

IN AN EARLY EXAMPLE OF 'EMPLOYMENT TRAINING', UNEMPLOYED GLASGOW WORKERS WERE HIRED BY THEIR CITY COUNCIL TO RENOVATE GLASGOW GREEN.

I FOUGHT IN THE NAPOLEONIC WARS FOR *THIS!*

CHARITY JUST PATCHES UP THE PROBLEM— IT DOESNAE CURE IT.

THE INEVITABLE CLASH ARRIVED IN 1820 — A WORKER'S UPRISING IN GLASGOW AND THE WEST OF SCOTLAND: THE SCOTTISH INSURRECTION

REVOLUTION

ALSO KNOWN AS THE RADICAL WAR

THIS WAS ESSENTIALLY A POPULAR UPRISING, INFILTRATED BY GOVERNMENT SPIES UNDER SPECIAL ORDERS. IT AIMED FOR UNIVERSAL SUFFRAGE, ANNUAL GENERAL ELECTIONS AND A SEPARATE SCOTTISH PARLIAMENT. GOVERNMENT AGENTS ENCOURAGED REBELS TO SET UP A 'PROVISIONAL GOVERNMENT,' WHOSE 'PROCLAMATION' WAS POSTED ON WALLS ALL OVER THE WEST OF SCOTLAND, URGING A GENERAL STRIKE AND UPRISING IN APRIL.

THERE IS REASON TO BELIEVE THE POSTER WAS THE WORK OF A GOVERNMENT AGENT, BUT IT HAD THE DESIRED EFFECT...

ABOUT 60,000 PEOPLE WENT ON IMMEDIATE STRIKE, TROOPS LINING THE STREETS OF GLASGOW.

HOWEVER, UNKNOWN TO MOST RADICAL FOLLOWERS, 28 'PROVISIONAL GOVERNMENT' MEMBERS HAD BEEN SECRETLY ARRESTED.

1st APRIL 1820...

300 RADICALS CLASHED WITH CAVALRY ON THE EVENING OF THE FIRST DAY (NO CASUALTIES).

BUT THE RADICALS BECAME ORGANISED. GLASGOW GREEN WAS USED AS A TRAINING GROUND BY THE PEOPLE'S ARMY. MEANWHILE, LANARKSHIRE CONTINGENTS RECRUITED MEMBERS AND COLLECTED ARMS AND AMMUNITION.

IN STRATHAVEN, LANARKSHIRE, MILITANTS MET IN THE HOUSE OF JAMES WILSON, A RADICAL WEAVER.

ON MONDAY APRIL 2ND, IT WAS DECIDED TO PREPARE FOR ARMED REVOLUTION. GUNS, PIKES AND AMMUNITION WERE PREPARED.

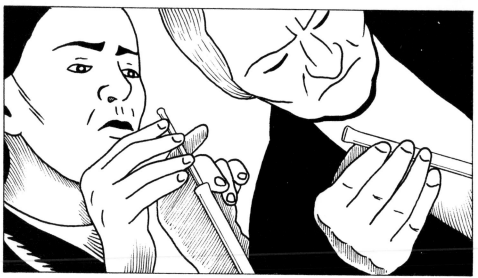

A MESSENGER ARRIVED FROM GLASGOW...

COUNTY RADICAL UNITS ARE MEETING UP TOMORROW ON THE CATHKIN BRAES, NEAR GLASGOW. AN ADVANCE ON GLASGOW IS PLANNED, TO JOIN CITY RADICALS IN A FULL SCALE ATTACK ON THE GOVERNMENT FORCES.

THAT NIGHT, THE STRATHAVEN RADICALS SEARCHED THE TOWN FOR ADDITIONAL WEAPONS AND RECRUITS.

BUT WHEN THE MESSENGER RETURNED...

GET AWAY AS QUICKLY AS YOU CAN! THE ARMY AND POLICE ARE ON THE ALERT!

SCOTLAND FREE OR A DESE

THE NEXT DAY, 50 ARMED MEN LEFT STRATHAVEN UNDER A RED BANNER READING 'SCOTLAND FREE OR A DESERT'.

WHEN THEY REACHED CATHKIN BRAES, IT WAS TO FIND THAT NO OTHER CONTINGENT HAD TURNED UP! A MESSENGER WAS SENT TO GLASGOW TO FIND OUT WHAT WAS HAPPENING. MEANWHILE, THEY WAITED AND RAISED THEIR FLAG OVER THE CLYDE VALLEY.

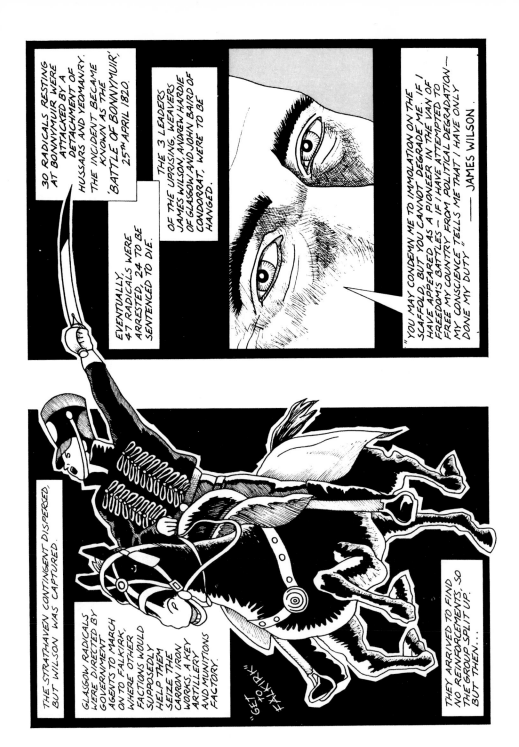

30 RADICALS RESTING AT BONNYMUIR WERE ATTACKED BY A DETACHMENT OF HUSSARS AND YEOMANRY. THE INCIDENT BECAME KNOWN AS THE 'BATTLE OF BONNYMUIR', 25TH APRIL 1820.

EVENTUALLY, 47 RADICALS WERE ARRESTED, 24 TO BE SENTENCED TO DIE.

THE 3 LEADERS OF THE UPRISING, WEAVERS JAMES WILSON, ANDREW HARDIE OF GLASGOW AND JOHN BAIRD OF CONDORRAT, WERE TO BE HANGED.

"YOU MAY CONDEMN ME TO IMMOLATION ON THE SCAFFOLD, BUT YOU CANNOT DEGRADE ME. IF I HAVE APPEARED AS A PIONEER IN THE VAN OF FREEDOM'S BATTLES – IF I HAVE ATTEMPTED TO FREE MY COUNTRY FROM POLITICAL DEGRADATION – MY CONSCIENCE TELLS ME THAT I HAVE ONLY DONE MY DUTY." — JAMES WILSON

THE STRATHAVEN CONTINGENT DISPERSED, BUT WILSON WAS CAPTURED.

GLASGOW RADICALS WERE DIRECTED BY GOVERNMENT AGENTS TO MARCH ON TO FALKIRK, WHERE OTHER FACTIONS WOULD SUPPOSEDLY HELP THEM SEIZE THE CARRON IRON WORKS, A KEY ARTILLERY AND MUNITIONS FACTORY.

"GET TO FALKIRK"

THEY ARRIVED TO FIND NO REINFORCEMENTS, SO THE GROUP SPLIT UP. BUT THEN....

BAIRD AND HARDIE WERE BOTH PUBLICLY HANGED AT STIRLING CASTLE, THEIR HEADS AFTERWARDS CHOPPED OFF AS THE CROWD CRIED IN PROTEST:

"MURDER!"

ON WEDNESDAY 30TH AUGUST 1820, WILSON WAS HANGED ON GLASGOW GREEN BEFORE A CROWD OF 20,000 PEOPLE WHO CRIED 'SHAME!' AND 'HE DIES FOR HIS COUNTRY!'. SOME PEOPLE - INCLUDING SOLDIERS - FAINTED AT THE SIGHT.

ANOTHER 19 RADICALS INVOLVED WERE TRANSPORTED.

REFORM ACT 1832

REFORM ACT 1884

A SERIES OF REFORM ACTS THROUGHOUT THE 19TH CENTURY INTRODUCED UNIVERSAL MANHOOD SUFFRAGE, GIVING THE WORKING MAN THE RIGHT TO VOTE.

BUT WOMEN REMAINED EXCLUDED.

WOMEN WERE TO BE DENIED THE RIGHT TO VOTE FOR WELL OVER 30 YEARS YET. (SCOTTISH WOMEN REMAIN POLITICALLY UNDER-REPRESENTED TO THIS DAY).

MEANWHILE, THE OLD CRAFT 'COMBINATIONS' HAD GIVEN WAY TO FEDERATED TRADE UNIONS, WHICH WOULD STRUGGLE FOR JUSTICE FOR ALL.

A NEW WAVE OF HIGHLAND CLEARANCES BEGAN, NOT ONLY TO MAKE WAY FOR SHEEP FARMING BUT NOW FOR EXPANDING GROUSE MOOR AND DEER FOREST TO CATER FOR THE SPORTING PRACTICES OF WEALTHY VICTORIAN TOURISTS.

BLAM BLAM

THOUSANDS OF TENANT FAMILIES WERE EVICTED BY THEIR LANDLORDS TO ACCOMODATE ENGLISH AND ANGLO-SCOTTISH UPPER CLASS HUNTING - AND - SHOOTING PARTIES.

"IN IRELAND LANDLORDS HAVE GONE TO THE LENGTH OF SWEEPING AWAY SEVERAL VILLAGES AT ONCE. IN SCOTLAND AREAS AS LARGE AS GERMAN PRINCIPALITIES ARE DEALT WITH" — MARX

HIGHLANDERS AND ISLANDERS FORMED THE **HIGHLAND LAND LEAGUE**, ORGANISING RENT STRIKES, SQUATTING AND SABOTAGE. AS EVICTIONS AND SUMMONSES FOR NON-PAYMENT OF RENT CONTINUED...

THE **CROFTERS' WAR** ERUPTED.

OFFICIALS WERE ATTACKED AND VIOLENT BATTLES BROKE OUT BETWEEN CROFTERS AND POLICE. TROOPS AND GUNBOATS WERE SENT TO THE HIGHLANDS AND ISLANDS TO PUT DOWN THE DISTURBANCE.

TO THIS DAY, THE HIGHLAND POPULATION HAS CONTINUED TO DECLINE THROUGH UNEMPLOYMENT AND ECONOMIC STAGNATION, AND MOST OF THE LAND IS STILL HELD BY BIG LANDOWNERS.

MEANWHILE, TRADE UNIONS ORGANISED AND HELPED RAISE POLITICAL CONSCIOUSNESS AMONG THE PEOPLE.

STRIKES, LOCKOUTS AND CLASHES WITH THE AUTHORITIES WERE COMMONPLACE IN THE LATE 19th AND EARLY 20th CENTURIES.

WAP!

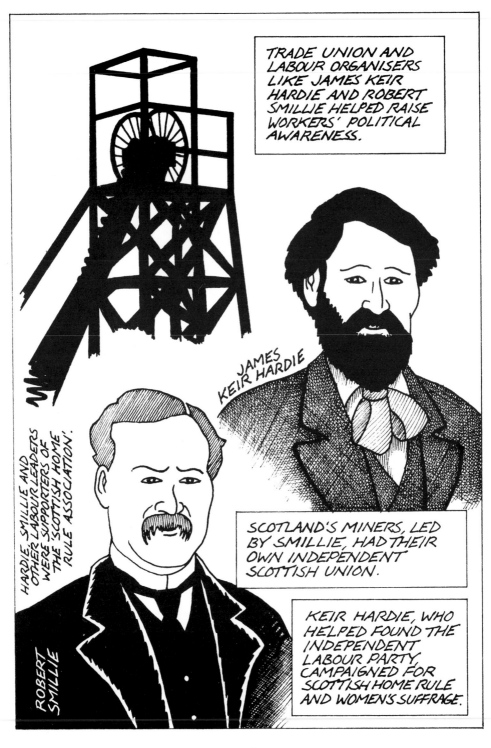

TRADE UNION AND LABOUR ORGANISERS LIKE JAMES KEIR HARDIE AND ROBERT SMILLIE HELPED RAISE WORKERS' POLITICAL AWARENESS.

JAMES KEIR HARDIE

HARDIE, SMILLIE AND OTHER LABOUR LEADERS WERE SUPPORTERS OF THE 'SCOTTISH HOME RULE ASSOCIATION'.

ROBERT SMILLIE

SCOTLAND'S MINERS, LED BY SMILLIE, HAD THEIR OWN INDEPENDENT SCOTTISH UNION.

KEIR HARDIE, WHO HELPED FOUND THE INDEPENDENT LABOUR PARTY, CAMPAIGNED FOR SCOTTISH HOME RULE AND WOMEN'S SUFFRAGE.

NORTHERN MEN'S
FEDERATION
FOR
WOMEN'S
SUFFRAGE

GLASGOW

MALE SUPPORT FOR WOMEN'S RIGHT TO VOTE WAS EXPRESSED INCREASINGLY THROUGH UNIONS, CHURCH AND LOCAL GOVERNMENT.

MEANWHILE, HOWEVER, WOMEN ORGANISED THEMSELVES, HOLDING MEETINGS THROUGHOUT SCOTLAND. ACTRESSES ANNIE MOFFAT AND MAGGIE FRASER WERE ARRESTED FOR THEIR ACTIVITIES.

"NOW'S THE DAY AND NOW'S THE HOUR"

GOVERNMENT REFUSAL OF THE WOMEN'S DEMANDS IN 1913 LED TO VIOLENCE. SUFFRAGETTES FIREBOMBED BUILDINGS ALL OVER SCOTLAND AND PUT ACID INTO LETTERBOXES. WOMEN WERE NOT GIVEN THE VOTE UNTIL AFTER THE FIRST WORLD WAR, DURING WHICH THEY HAD BEEN EMPLOYED IN THE 'TRADITIONAL' INDUSTRIAL WORK OF MEN.

VOTES FOR WOMEN
WOMEN'S FREEDOM LEAGUE
SCOTTISH CAMPAIGN

GLASGOW, JANUARY 1919...
80,000 PEOPLE STOPPED WORK, DEMANDING
A 40-HOUR WEEK (WITHOUT LOSS OF PAY)
TO EASE UNEMPLOYMENT.
THE GOVERNMENT, FEARING REVOLUTION,
SENT 12,000 **ENGLISH** TROOPS TO KEEP
ORDER.

SIX TANKS WERE STATIONED AT THE
CATTLE MARKET, READY FOR USE.

GEORGE SQUARE, GLASGOW, 31st JANUARY 1919

AN ENORMOUS, RED-FLAG-WAVING CROWD DEMONSTRATED AND RIOTED OUTSIDE THE CITY CHAMBERS, OVERTURNING A POLICE TRAMCAR AND CHASING THE POLICE OFF. BUT MOUNTED POLICE REINFORCEMENTS SOON CLEARED THE AREA WITH BATONS.

ONE OF THE MOST MEMORABLE NAMES OF THIS PERIOD IS THAT OF **JOHN MACLEAN (1879 - 1923),** THE PROMINENT WORKERS' LEADER WHO IDENTIFIED THE INTERNATIONAL CAUSE OF THE PEOPLE WITH A NEED TO END IMPERIALISM, ADVOCATING A 'SOCIALIST REPUBLIC OF SCOTLAND' WITH GLASGOW AS THE CAPITAL.

MACLEAN'S WORKING CLASS PARENTS WERE VICTIMS OF THE HIGHLAND CLEARANCES WHO SETTLED IN GLASGOW.

MACLEAN BECAME A GRADUATE OF GLASGOW UNIVERSITY AND A QUALIFIED SCHOOLTEACHER.

HE RESOLVED TO USE HIS EDUCATION FOR THE BENEFIT OF THE WORKING CLASS.

BY 1900 HE WAS TEACHING SCHOOLCHILDREN BY DAY AND RUNNING A WEEKLY ADULT NIGHT CLASS.

THE EVENING CLASS, HOWEVER, WAS NOT ADULT EDUCATION IN THE ORTHODOX SENSE —

IT WAS THE EDUCATION OF WORKERS IN REVOLUTIONARY SOCIALISM, MARXIST ECONOMICS AND WORKING CLASS HISTORY.

POWER DEPENDS ON OWNERSHIP AND CONTROL OF PRODUCTION

SOCIALISM
→ SOCIALIST economy rule by the PROLETARIAT

LIBERALISM
→ CAPITALIST economy rule by the BOURGOISIE

CONSERVATISM
→ FEUDAL economy rule by the ARISTOCRACY

MANY LEADING TRADE UNIONISTS AND 'RED CLYDESIDERS' WERE STUDENTS AT MACLEAN'S NIGHT SCHOOL.

MACLEAN WAS IMPRISONED 5 TIMES DURING AND AFTER THE FIRST WORLD WAR (WHICH HE AND HIS 'RED CLYDESIDERS' OPPOSED). HE ORGANISED STRIKES AND WORKERS' COMMITTEES, ORGANISATIONS AND INSTITUTIONS, ATTEMPTING TO ENCOURAGE NON-VIOLENT REVOLUTION.

N.B.— THE LABOUR MOVEMENT IN SCOTLAND AT THIS TIME DEMANDED A SCOTTISH PARLIAMENT WITH ECONOMIC OWNERSHIP AND CONTROL.

A JOINT CAMPAIGN BY THE LABOUR PARTY AND THE HIGHLAND LAND LEAGUE STATED THAT ENGLAND SHOWED A DISPOSITION TO CONSERVATISM WHILE THE SCOTTISH PEOPLE ARE PROGRESSIVE IN THEIR ATTITUDES.

THE SOCIAL REVOLUTION IS POSSIBLE SOONER IN SCOTLAND RATHER THAN IN ENGLAND... SCOTTISH SEPARATION IS PART OF THE PROCESS OF ENGLAND'S IMPERIAL DISINTEGRATION AND IS A HELP TOWARDS THE ULTIMATE TRIUMPH OF THE WORKERS OF THE WORLD.

HE REFUSED TO JOIN THE COMMUNIST PARTY OF GREAT BRITAIN, REJECTING ITS CENTRALISM AND PARTY AUTHORITY. HE FORMED THE SCOTTISH WORKERS' REPUBLICAN PARTY, AIMING FOR A SCOTTISH SOCIALIST REPUBLIC. HE DIED OF PNEUMONIA IN 1923.

SCOTLAND'S M.P.s (29 LABOUR, 1 COMMUNIST IN 1922) WERE SCORNED IN WESTMINSTER BY TRADITIONAL TORY M.P.s (OR EVEN SUSPENDED FROM THE HOUSE) FOR BEING TOO OUTSPOKEN OR FOR QUESTIONING THE SPEAKER'S 'IMPARTIALITY'.

JIMMY MAXTON, I.L.P. LEADER. FRIEND AND FORMER STUDENT OF JOHN MACLEAN.

ROMANTIC INFLUENCES OF BURNS AND SCOTT WERE COMBINED WITH SOCIALIST POLITICS TO PRODUCE POETRY IN THE SCOTS DIALECT RELATING TO SOCIAL AND POLITICAL ISSUES.

MACDIAIRMID WAS A FOUNDER MEMBER OF THE NATIONAL PARTY OF SCOTLAND, BUT WAS EXPELLED FOR HIS *RADICAL* VIEWS. HE NEXT TRIED THE COMMUNIST PARTY OF GREAT BRITAIN, WHO THEN EXPELLED HIM FOR HIS SCOTTISH *NATIONALIST* VIEWS.

YE CANNAE WIN !

HE REMAINED A COMMITTED SOCIALIST AND PATRIOT ALL HIS LIFE, WRITING POETRY, ESSAYS AND PROSE THROUGHOUT THE 20th CENTURY UNTIL HIS DEATH IN 1978.

MACDIAIRMID BELIEVED THAT SCOTTISH CULTURE WAS BEING ERODED BY ENGLISH CULTURE AND THAT THIS HELPS ENGLAND RETAIN ITS HOLD ON SCOTLAND.

ECONOMIC DEPRESSION THROUGHOUT THE 1920's CAUSED 400,000 SCOTS TO EMIGRATE.

ENGLISH VOTES IN THE 1922 ELECTION PUT THE CONSERVATIVES IN POWER. THE FOLLOWING YEAR, LABOUR WERE ELECTED. SCOTSMAN RAMSAY MACDONALD, BRITAIN'S FIRST LABOUR PRIME MINISTER, FORMED A COALITION WITH THE CONSERVATIVES AND LIBERALS, MODERATING HIS POLICIES.

A 'LUM HAT' GOVERNMENT LIKE A' THE REST !

PROMISES OF SOCIALIST REFORM AND HOME RULE TURNED TO EXCUSES, AND BOTH SCOTLAND AND THE LABOUR MOVEMENT FELT BETRAYED.
A GENERAL STRIKE AND CHANGES OF GOVERNMENT MADE LITTLE DIFFERENCE THROUGHOUT THE '20's AND '30's. ANTI-UNEMPLOYMENT AND HUNGER MARCHES EXPRESSED PEOPLE'S FRUSTRATION.

EMPIRE
EXHIBITION
SCOTLAND 1938

SCOTLAND

THE EMPIRE EXHIBITION, HELD IN GLASGOW IN 1938, THOUGH VISUALLY IMPRESSIVE, WAS A MERE COSMETIC, DISGUISING THE REALITY OF POVERTY AND THE COMING THREAT OF WAR.

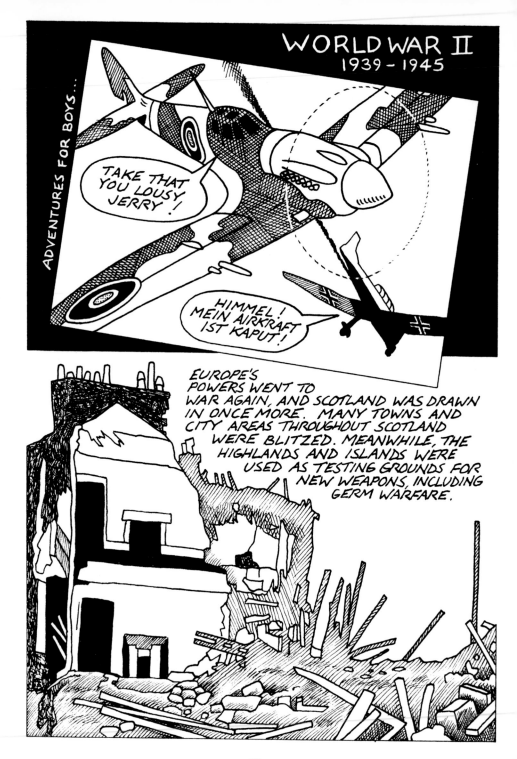

57,720 SCOTS DIED IN THE SECOND WORLD WAR. AFTER THE WAR, A NEW AGE OF PROSPERITY PROMISED BY THE GOVERNMENT FAILED TO REACH EXPECTATIONS.

ALTHOUGH A FEW NEW TOWNS AND INDUSTRIAL ESTATES WERE CREATED, SCOTLAND DID NOT PROSPER NEARLY AS MUCH AS ENGLAND.

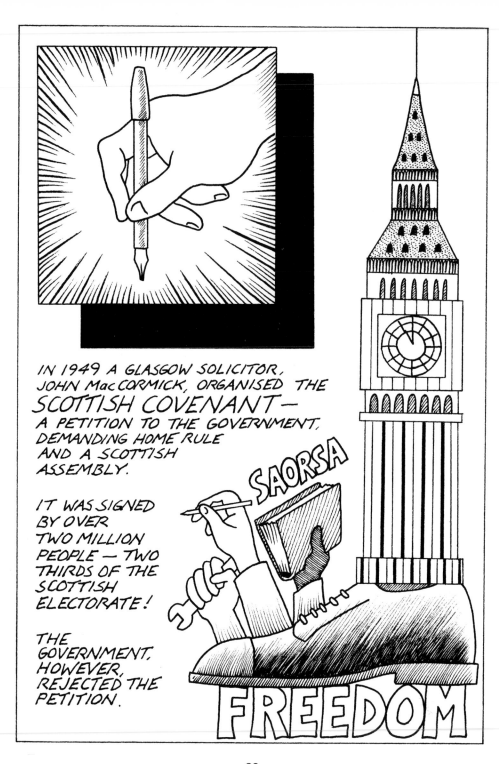

IN 1949 A GLASGOW SOLICITOR,
JOHN MacCORMICK, ORGANISED THE
SCOTTISH COVENANT—
A PETITION TO THE GOVERNMENT,
DEMANDING HOME RULE
AND A SCOTTISH
ASSEMBLY.

IT WAS SIGNED
BY OVER
TWO MILLION
PEOPLE — TWO
THIRDS OF THE
SCOTTISH
ELECTORATE!

THE
GOVERNMENT,
HOWEVER,
REJECTED THE
PETITION.

SAORSA

FREEDOM

ON CHRISTMAS DAY, 1950, A GROUP OF YOUNG SCOTTISH STUDENTS (MEMBERS OF THE 'SCOTTISH PATRIOTS'), REAPPROPRIATED THE STONE OF DESTINY FROM UNDER THE CORONATION THRONE IN WESTMINSTER ABBEY.

THE ENGLISH PRESS WERE OUTRAGED BY THE SHEER CHEEK OF THE ACT, DESCRIBING IT AS 'SACRILEGE' AND 'THEFT' (EVEN THOUGH IT WAS STOLEN FROM SCOTLAND IN THE FIRST PLACE BY EDWARD I). AFTER NEGOTIATION, THE STUDENTS AGREED TO PUT THE STONE IN ARBROATH ABBEY, WHERE POLICE SEIZED IT AND ULTIMATELY RETURNED IT TO WESTMINSTER.

THE 'SCOTTISH PATRIOTS' LED BY WENDY WOOD, AND OTHER GROUPS AND INDIVIDUALS CARRIED OUT SMALL EXTREMIST TACTICS OF PROTEST. PILLAR BOXES BEARING THE INSIGNIA 'E II R' WERE GELIGNITED OR OTHERWISE DAMAGED.

IN THE 1950's, SCOTLAND'S TRADITIONAL INDUSTRIES WERE BECOMING UNPRODUCTIVE AND OUTDATED.

LONDON FINANCIERS POURED MONEY INTO DEVELOPING THE ENGLISH MIDLANDS, BUT SAW NO POINT IN MODERNISING SCOTLAND, WHERE OLD INDUSTRIES EARNED A GOOD SHORT-TERM PROFIT. SCOTLAND'S ECONOMY WAS (STILL IS) MAINLY ENGLISH (AND INCREASINGLY AMERICAN) OWNED. SUCCESSFUL SCOTTISH COMPANIES MOVED THEIR HEADQUARTERS TO LONDON OR WERE ABSORBED BY BIGGER ENGLISH FIRMS.

NATIONALISATION WAS INTRODUCED...

PUBLIC OWNERSHIP? SOUNDS GREAT!

NO. ALL IT MEANS IS CENTRALISED ECONOMIC CONTROL FROM LONDON.

WE SHALL PLAN A NEW BRITAIN FROM LONDON.

PRIME MINISTER CLEMENT ATTLEE OPPOSED SCOTTISH HOME RULE IN ANY FORM. THIS LED TO HIS LOSS OF SUPPORT IN SCOTLAND.

THE SHIPYARDS BEGAN TO DECLINE, DUE TO MODERNISED OVERSEAS COMPETITION. UNEMPLOYMENT BEGAN TO RISE AGAIN.

YOU'VE NEVER HAD IT SO GOOD!

HAROLD MACMILLAN, TORY PRIME MINISTER.

SCOTLAND DID NOT AGREE, AND VOTED LABOUR IN THE 1959 ELECTION.

BUT ENGLISH VOTES BROUGHT THE CONSERVATIVES BACK INTO POWER.

BAN THE BOMB

WOMEN AGAINST THE BOMB

SUCCESSIVE GOVERNMENTS THROUGH-OUT THE '60s ATTEMPTED TO MODERNISE SCOTTISH INDUSTRY, BUT THE EFFORTS WERE 'TOO LITTLE, TOO LATE'. SCOTLAND NEVER PROSPERED AS MUCH AS ENGLAND, AND SCOTTISH WORKERS WERE OFTEN PAID LESS THAN THEIR ENGLISH COUNTERPARTS.

BESIDES, THE OLD INDUSTRIES DIED BEFORE NEW ONES COULD BE CREATED. UNEMPLOYMENT KEPT RISING AND INDUSTRY DECLINED.

SCOTTISH INDUSTRY

THE CAMPAIGNING 60s.

IN THE 1970 GENERAL ELECTION, ENGLISH VOTES PUT EDWARD HEATH INTO POWER. HEATH MET SEVERAL STRIKES AND CONFRONTATIONS DURING HIS TERM OF OFFICE.

WHEN THE UPPER CLYDE SHIPYARDS WERE THREATENED WITH CLOSURE IN 1971, 80,000 WENT ON STRIKE AND 200,000 SCOTTISH WORKERS STOPPED WORK IN SYMPATHY.

BUT SCOTLAND'S DEPENDENCE ON ENGLISH-OWNED HEAVY INDUSTRY LED TO IT'S DOWNFALL.

HEE HEE HEE

MANY SAW THE DISCOVERY OF OIL RESOURCES OFF THE
SCOTTISH COAST AS OFFERING SCOTLAND NEW HOPE.

AN EXPLOSIVE SITUATION...

AN UPSURGE OF NATIONALIST SUPPORT PRESSED LABOUR
INTO RENEWED COMMITMENT TOWARDS HOME RULE.

TERRORISM—NO!

MEANWHILE, SPECIAL TROOPS WERE TRAINED IN ANTI-
GUERRILLA TACTICS IN CASE THE OIL RIGS WERE SEIZED
BY SCOTTISH EXTREMISTS.
(THOUGH THE OIL RIGS WERE NOT ATTACKED, INCIDENTS
OF EXTREMIST VIOLENCE DID OCCUR, BUT WERE LARGELY
COVERED UP BY THE AUTHORITIES OR PLAYED DOWN BY
THE MEDIA). HOWEVER, SUCH INCIDENTS WERE RARE AND
LACKED POPULAR SUPPORT. DESPITE BOMB ATTACKS ON OIL
PIPELINES, ETC., THERE WERE NO HUMAN CASUALTIES.

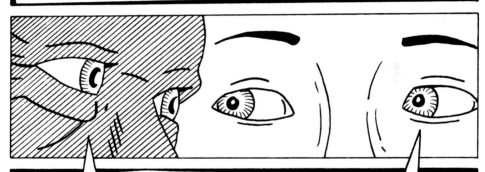

THE SCOTTISH ASSEMBLY OFFERED
BY JIM CALLAGHAN'S LABOUR
GOVERNMENT WOULD ONLY HAVE
ADMINISTRATIVE (NOT DECISION-
MAKING) POWERS.

THIS
WAS CLEARLY NOT
ENOUGH FOR THE
SCOTS, WHO EXPRESSED
DISAPPROVAL...

MASS ACTION—YES!

IN A REFERENDUM HELD IN 1979 THE ELECTORATE,
DISILLUSIONED AND SCEPTICAL, LARGELY ABSTAINED, FAILING
TO REACH THE 40% MAJORITY REQUIRED TO BRING ABOUT
THE ASSEMBLY.

BUT OF THOSE WHO DID VOTE, A CLEAR MAJORITY SAID 'YES'.

AND THEN, IN THE GENERAL ELECTION OF 1979, CAME THE
MOST CRUSHING BLOW TO SCOTLAND IN MODERN TIMES...

DESPITE THE EXPRESS FEELINGS OF THE MAJORITY OF SCOTS, ENGLISH 'HOME COUNTIES' VOTES ELECTED *MARGARET THATCHER* TO PREMIERSHIP. SCOTLAND HAD VOTED ANTI-TORY, BUT WAS TO GET A TORY GOVERNMENT — AND BE PUNISHED.

SCHOOLS, HOSPITALS AND OTHER PUBLIC SERVICES WERE CUT.

INDUSTRIES WERE CLOSED DOWN OR SOLD OFF.

SHE TRIED TO CHANGE THE ATTITUDES OF THE SCOTS.

I THINK IT'S TIME THESE SCOTS WERE PUT IN THEIR PLACE ONCE AND FOR ALL.

WHILE TALKING OF 'DEMOCRACY', HER DEMEANOUR WAS DICTATORIAL.

SHE ENCOURAGED TOADYING AND SNOBBERY.

SHE CONDEMNED WHAT SHE CALLED SCOTLAND'S 'COUNCIL HOUSE MENTALITY' — A SENSE OF COMMUNITY SHE COULD NOT UNDERSTAND. SHE TRIED TO ENCOURAGE RUTHLESS PRIVATE COMPETITION AND SELF-SEEKING BEHAVIOUR.

THATCHER CLAIMED TO HAVE 'LIBERATED' SCOTLAND, ARROGANTLY IMPLYING THAT SHE KNEW BETTER THAN THE 'SCOTS WHAT SCOTLAND'S BEST INTERESTS WERE.

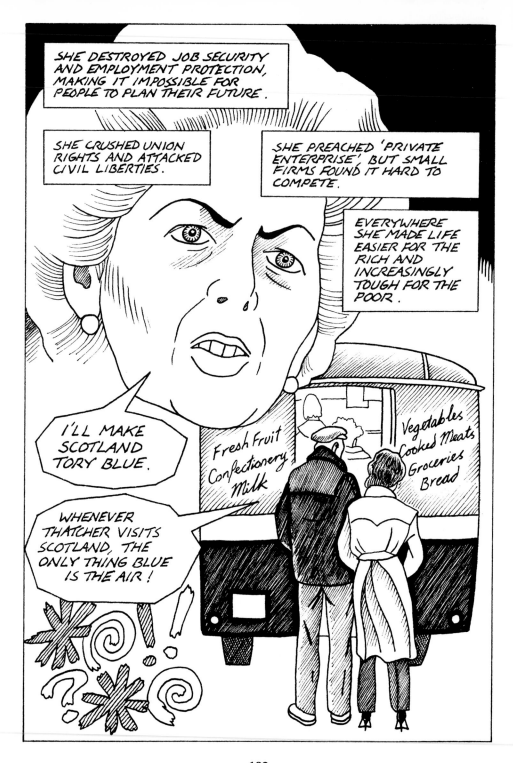

WHEN BRITAIN BEGAN TO IMPORT FOREIGN COAL, SCOTLAND'S MINERS JOINED THE NATIONAL MINER'S STRIKE TO FIGHT CLOSURES. THE STRIKE WAS BEATEN AND (WITH ONLY ONE EXCEPTION) ALL COAL MINES IN SCOTLAND CLOSED.

THATCHER INTRODUCED A NEW LOCAL TAX SYSTEM - THE COMMUNITY CHARGE OR POLL TAX - A VERY UNEQUAL SYSTEM WHICH REMAINS WIDELY HATED. SHE DECIDED, BY WAY OF EXPERIMENT, TO TRY IT OUT ON SCOTLAND FIRST, TO TEST RESPONSE BEFORE IMPOSING IT ON THE REST OF BRITAIN.

40,000 PEOPLE MARCHED IN GLASGOW IN PROTEST. A MILLION SCOTS REFUSE TO PAY, DESPITE THREATS OF 'WARRANT SALES' OF THEIR BELONGINGS.

WHAT REALLY ANGERED PEOPLE ABOUT THE POLL TAX, HOWEVER, WAS THAT SCOTLAND WAS USED AS A 'GUINEA PIG'!

STUFF YER POLL TAX!

SCOTS - GET OFF YOUR KNEES

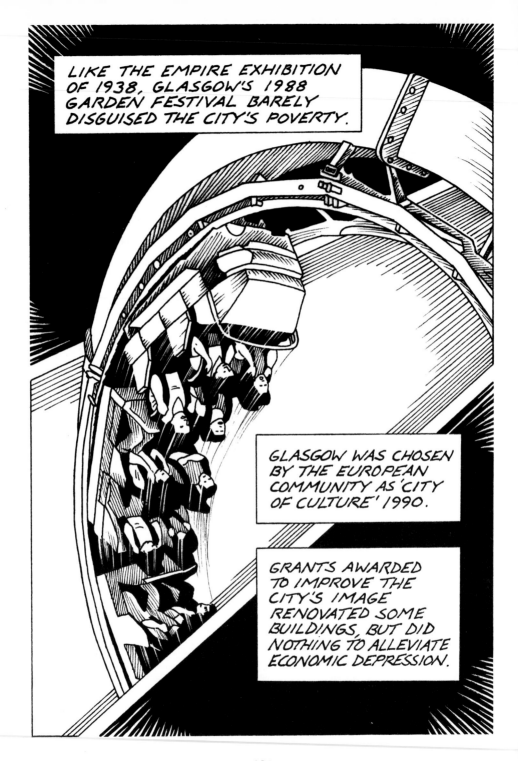

LIKE THE EMPIRE EXHIBITION OF 1938, GLASGOW'S 1988 GARDEN FESTIVAL BARELY DISGUISED THE CITY'S POVERTY.

GLASGOW WAS CHOSEN BY THE EUROPEAN COMMUNITY AS 'CITY OF CULTURE' 1990.

GRANTS AWARDED TO IMPROVE THE CITY'S IMAGE RENOVATED SOME BUILDINGS, BUT DID NOTHING TO ALLEVIATE ECONOMIC DEPRESSION.

-107-

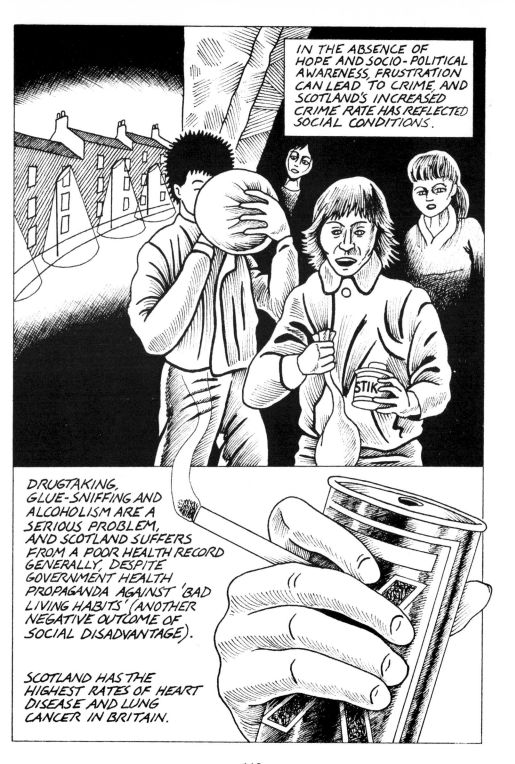

IN THE ABSENCE OF HOPE AND SOCIO-POLITICAL AWARENESS, FRUSTRATION CAN LEAD TO CRIME, AND SCOTLAND'S INCREASED CRIME RATE HAS REFLECTED SOCIAL CONDITIONS.

DRUGTAKING, GLUE-SNIFFING AND ALCOHOLISM ARE A SERIOUS PROBLEM, AND SCOTLAND SUFFERS FROM A POOR HEALTH RECORD GENERALLY, DESPITE GOVERNMENT HEALTH PROPAGANDA AGAINST 'BAD LIVING HABITS' (ANOTHER NEGATIVE OUTCOME OF SOCIAL DISADVANTAGE).

SCOTLAND HAS THE HIGHEST RATES OF HEART DISEASE AND LUNG CANCER IN BRITAIN.

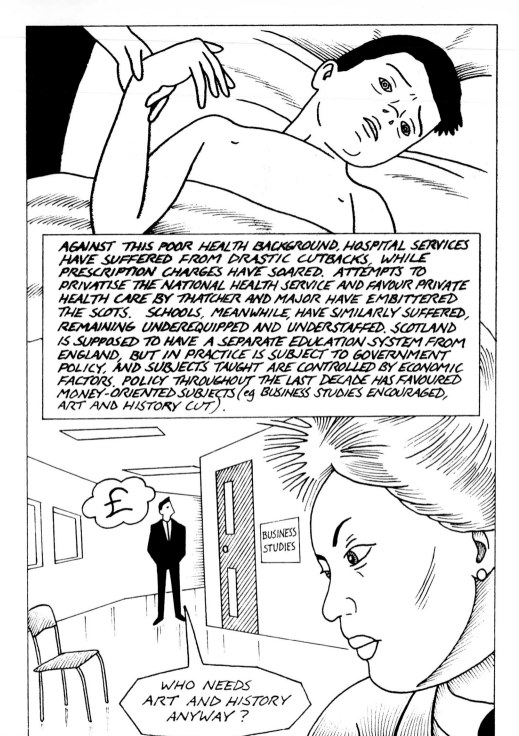

AGAINST THIS POOR HEALTH BACKGROUND, HOSPITAL SERVICES HAVE SUFFERED FROM DRASTIC CUTBACKS, WHILE PRESCRIPTION CHARGES HAVE SOARED. ATTEMPTS TO PRIVATISE THE NATIONAL HEALTH SERVICE AND FAVOUR PRIVATE HEALTH CARE BY THATCHER AND MAJOR HAVE EMBITTERED THE SCOTS. SCHOOLS, MEANWHILE, HAVE SIMILARLY SUFFERED, REMAINING UNDEREQUIPPED AND UNDERSTAFFED. SCOTLAND IS SUPPOSED TO HAVE A SEPARATE EDUCATION SYSTEM FROM ENGLAND, BUT IN PRACTICE IS SUBJECT TO GOVERNMENT POLICY, AND SUBJECTS TAUGHT ARE CONTROLLED BY ECONOMIC FACTORS. POLICY THROUGHOUT THE LAST DECADE HAS FAVOURED MONEY-ORIENTED SUBJECTS (eg BUSINESS STUDIES ENCOURAGED, ART AND HISTORY CUT).

BUSINESS STUDIES

WHO NEEDS ART AND HISTORY ANYWAY?

ECONOMIC DECLINE HAS TAKEN A SEVERE TOLL ON SCOTLAND.

SCOTLAND'S ECONOMY IS VIRTUALLY UNDER ENGLISH, AMERICAN AND FOREIGN OWNERSHIP AND CONTROL.

E.C. PROPOSALS TO ALLOW SCOTLAND A MORE INDEPENDENT VOICE IN ECONOMIC MATTERS REMAIN TO BE TESTED. BUT SCOTLAND'S DEPENDENT 'REGIONAL' STATUS IS UNLIKELY TO CHANGE UNDER THE STATUS QUO.

'ENTERPRISE INITIATIVE' SCHEMES HAVE LARGELY FAILED, SMALL CONCERNS BEING UNABLE TO COMPETE AGAINST LARGER FIRMS.

SCOTLAND HAS NO TAX-RAISING POWERS OF ITS OWN.

ENGLAND TAXES US, BUT WE GET LITTLE IN THE WAY OF PUBLIC SPENDING IN RETURN.

MANY INDUSTRIES HAVE BEEN CLOSED DOWN AND THE MORE SUCCESSFUL NATIONALISED INDUSTRIES SOLD OFF TO PRIVATE OWNERSHIP. SCOTLAND HAS ABSOLUTELY NO SAY IN THE DEGREE OR TYPE OF PUBLIC OWNERSHIP ITS PEOPLE WANT.

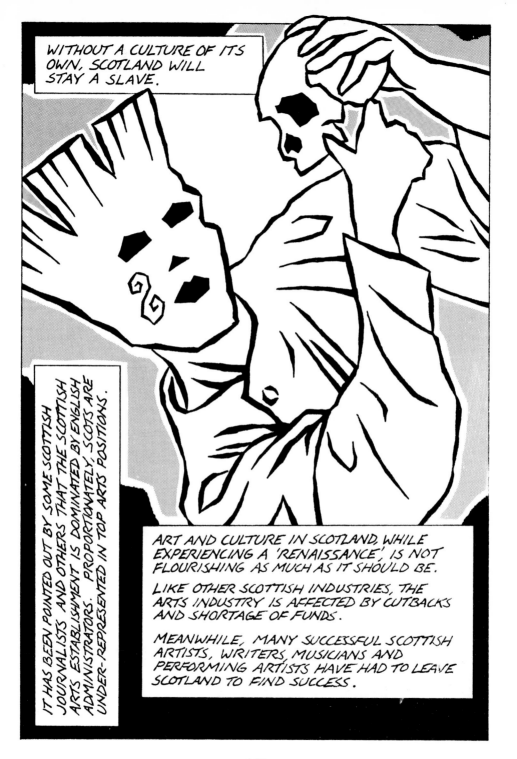

WITHOUT A CULTURE OF ITS OWN, SCOTLAND WILL STAY A SLAVE.

IT HAS BEEN POINTED OUT BY SOME SCOTTISH JOURNALISTS AND OTHERS THAT THE SCOTTISH ARTS ESTABLISHMENT IS DOMINATED BY ENGLISH ADMINISTRATORS. PROPORTIONATELY, SCOTS ARE UNDER-REPRESENTED IN TOP ARTS POSITIONS.

ART AND CULTURE IN SCOTLAND, WHILE EXPERIENCING A 'RENAISSANCE', IS NOT FLOURISHING AS MUCH AS IT SHOULD BE.

LIKE OTHER SCOTTISH INDUSTRIES, THE ARTS INDUSTRY IS AFFECTED BY CUTBACKS AND SHORTAGE OF FUNDS.

MEANWHILE, MANY SUCCESSFUL SCOTTISH ARTISTS, WRITERS, MUSICIANS AND PERFORMING ARTISTS HAVE HAD TO LEAVE SCOTLAND TO FIND SUCCESS.

THE TOURIST INDUSTRY IMPORTS CHEAP TARTAN GOODS, KILLING LOCAL CRAFT INDUSTRIES AND PERPETUATING THE 'HARRY LAUDER' IMAGE.
COMMERCIALISATION OF THE TARTAN-AND-HEATHER PSEUDOCULTURE PATRONISES AND RIDICULES THE SCOTS.

SCOTLAND IS A NUCLEAR DUMPING GROUND FOR ENGLAND.

SCOTLAND'S ENVIRONMENT SUFFERS FROM POLLUTION (MUCH OF IT FROM ENGLAND). THE ONCE IMMACULATE LOCHS AND RIVERS OF THE HIGHLANDS ARE CONTAMINATED WITH ACID RAIN. MEANWHILE, NUCLEAR WASTE IS STORED IN SCOTLAND — FAR FROM LONDON, WHERE THE DECISION WAS MADE. THE SCOTS HAD NO SAY IN THE MATTER (OF COURSE).

NON-NUCLEAR TOXIC WASTE IS ALSO STORED.

Pandora's HIGHLAND SHORTBREAD

RADIOACTIVE

DANGER

SCOTLAND IS ALSO A NUCLEAR MISSILE BASE FOR ENGLAND AND N.A.T.O.

... AND THEREFORE A TARGET.

SCOTTISH CND
PROTEST AND SURVIVE

SCOTLAND HAS NO CONTROL OVER ITS OWN DEFENCE MATTERS...

...E.G. NEUTRALITY, NUCLEAR DISARMAMENT, ETC.

UNCONFIRMED REPORTS CLAIM THAT M.O.D. WORKERS AT NUCLEAR BASES ARE POLITICALLY VETTED FOR 'SUBVERSIVE' OPINIONS.

IT IS ESTIMATED THAT, IN THE EVENT OF EVEN A 'SMALL SCALE' NUCLEAR ATTACK, WE WOULD LOSE 90% OF OUR POPULATION.

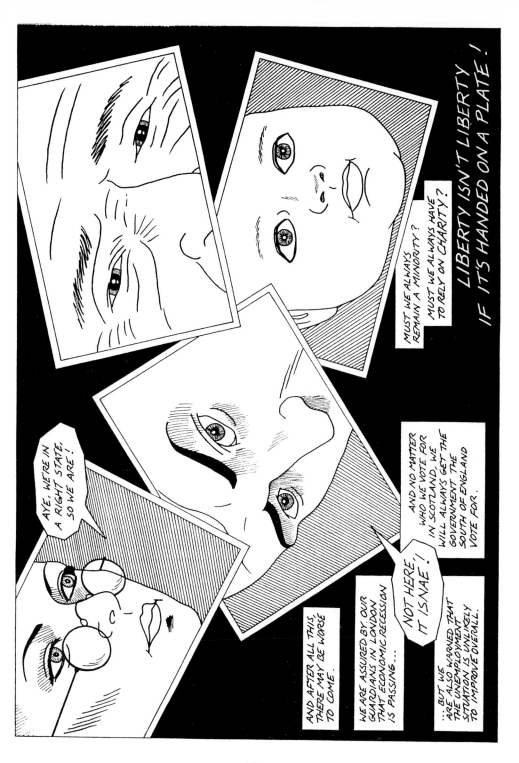

BUT ALL IS NOT DOOM AND GLOOM.

THERE IS HOPE.

IT IS TRUE THAT, BEYOND THE TARTAN GIFT SHOPS AND THE TOURIST WOOLEN MILLS, THE REAL SCOTLAND IS A DEPRIVED NATION...
BUT THE SCOTS ARE NOT A PATHETIC, DEFEATED PEOPLE.

CLOSED

A NEW TIDE IS TURNING ...

HOME RULE NEED NOT MEAN MUTUAL EXCLUSION BETWEEN SCOTLAND AND ENGLAND.

WE CAN BE PARTNERS RATHER THAN RIVALS.

BUT THERE IS A GROWING CONSCIOUSNESS IN SCOTLAND WHICH MAKES ONE THING CLEAR:

HOME RULE—TO WHATEVER DEGREE—MUST ENSURE SCOTLAND AND ENGLAND ARE *ABSOLUTELY EQUAL*!

BIBLIOGRAPHY

Scotland 2000. CARGILL, Kenneth (Ed) (BBC 1987)

The Scottish Insurrection of 1820. MAC A-GHOB-HAINN, Seamus and ELLIS, Peter Berresford. (Pluto Press, 1970)

Labour In Scotland. MACDOUGALL, Iain. (Mainstream 1985)

John Maclean. MILTON, Nan. (Pluto Press 1973)

A Century Of The Scottish People. SMOUT, T.C. (Fontana 1986)

Scotland's Story. STEEL, Tom. (Fontana, 1985)

Various other history books and enclyclopediae were also consulted for reference.

Other sources included pamphlets and publications by the Campaign for a Scottish Assembly, the Labour Party, the Scottish Constitutional Assembly, the Scottish National Party, the Scottish Socialist Party, the Scottish T.U.C., the Scottish Republican Socialist Party, the *Scots Independent* newspaper and the magazine Radical Scotland.

OTHER BOOKS FROM LUATH PRESS

THE CROFTING YEARS. Francis Thompson. A remarkable and moving study of crofting in the Highlands and Islands. It tells of the bloody conflicts a century ago when the crofters and their families faced all the forces of law and order, and demanded a legal status and security of tenure, and of how gunboats cruised the Western Isles in Government's classic answer. Life in the crofting townships is described with great insight and affection. Food, housing, healing and song are all dealt with. But the book is no nostalgic longing for the past. It looks to the future and argues that crofting must be carefully nurtured as a reservoir of potential strength for an uncertain future.

Frank Thompson lives and works in Stornoway. His life has been intimately bound up with the crofters, and he well knows of what he writes.

ISBN 0 946487 06 5. Paperback. £4:75p.

BARE FEET AND TACKETY BOOTS. Archie Cameron. The author is the last survivor who those who were born and reared on the island of Rhum in the days before the First World War, when the island was the private playground of a rich absentee landowner. Archie recalls all the pleasures and pains of those days. He writes of the remarkable characters, not least his own father, who worked the estate and guided the Gentry in their search for stags and fish. The Gentry have left ample records of their time on the island, but little is known of those who lived and worked there. Archie fills this gap. He recalls the pains and pleasures of his boyhood. Factors and Schoolmasters, midges and fish, deer and ducks and shepherds, the joys of poaching, the misery of MacBraynes' steamers -- they are all here.

This book is an important piece of social history, but, much more, it is a fascinating record of a way of life gone not so long ago, but already almost forgotten.

ISBN 0 946487 17 0. Paperback. £5:95p

TALES OF THE NORTH COAST. Alan Temperley and the pupils of Farr Secondary School. In this collection of 58 tales, there is a memorial to the great tradition of Highland story-telling. Simply told and unadorned, these tales are wide-ranging -- historical dramas, fairy tales, great battles, ship-wreck and ghosts, Highland rogues -- they all appear in this gallimaufry of tales, many of which have been told and re-told for generations round the fireside.

In addition to the tales, Alan Temperley has collected together a series of contemporary writings about the Clearances of Strathnaver, a central feature of local history, and a tragedy whose effects are still felt and discussed.

ISBN 0 946487 18 9 Paperback. £5:95.

MOUNTAIN DAYS AND BOTHY NIGHTS. Dave Brown and Ian Mitchell. The authors have climbed, walked and bothied over much of Scotland for many years. There could be no better guide to the astonishing variety of bothies, howffs and dosses on the Scottish hills. They were part of the great explosion of climbing in the Fifties and Sixties, and they write of this with first-hand knowledge, sympathy and understanding.

Fishgut Mac, Desperate Dan, Stumpy and the Big Yin may not be on the hills any more, but the bothies and howffs they used are still there. There was the Royal Bothy, paid for by the Queen herself after an encounter with a gang of anarchist, republican hill-climbing despera-does. There was the Secret Howff, built under the very noses of the disapproving laird and his gamekeepers. There was the Tarff Hotel, with its Three Star A.A. rating. These, and many more, feature in this book, together with tales of climbs and walks in the days of bendy boots and no artificial aids.

ISBN 0 946487 15 4. Paperback. £5:95p.

TALL TALES FROM AN ISLAND. Peter Macnab. These tales come from the island of Mull, but they could just as well come from anywhere in the Highlands and Islands. Witches, ghosts, warlocks and fairies abound, as do stories of the people, their quiet humour and their abiding wit. A book to dip into, laugh over, and enthuse about. Out of this great range of stories a general picture emerges of an island people, stubborn and strong in adversity, but warm and co-operative and totally wedded to their island way of life. It is a clear picture of a microcosmic society perfectly adapted to an environment that, in spite of its great beauty, can be harsh and unforgiving.

Peter Macnab was born and grew up on Mull, and he knows and loves every inch of it. Not for him the 'superiority' of the incomer who makes joke cardboard figures of the island people and their ways. He presents a rounded account of Mull and its people.

ISBN 0 946487 07 3. Paperback. £6:50p.

COME DUNGEONS DARK. John Caldwell. The Life and Times of Guy Aldred, Glasgow Anarchist. Hardly a street-corner site in Glasgow did not know Guy Aldred's great resonant voice belabouring the evils of society. Hardly a Glasgow voter for three generations did not have the opportunity of electing him to the city or national government he despised so much, and vowed to enter only on his own terms if elected. But he never was elected, although he once stood simultaneously for fourteen city wards. He claimed there was better company in Barlinnie Prison (which he knew well) than in the Corridors of Power.

Guy Alfred Aldred was born on November 5th 1886, and died on 16th October 1963. He had just 10 pence in his pocket when he died. Boy-preacher, Social Democrat, Prisoner of Conscience, Conscientious Objector, Anarcho-Communist, orater, writer, publisher -- Guy Aldred never ceased struggling for those things in which he believed. He was part of Glasgow's history, and must never be forgotten.

ISBN 0 946487 19 7. Paperback. Price £6:95p.

SEVEN STEPS IN THE DARK. Bob Smith. The writer of this book went into the pit when he was fourteen years old, to work with his father. They toiled in a low seam, just a few inches high, lying in the coal dust and mud, getting out the coal with pick and shovel. Bob spent his whole working life in the pits of Scotland, until injury forced his retirement. This is his story, but it is also the story of the last forty years of Scottish coalmining.

A staunch Trades Unionist, Bob was a Lodge official for many years, sacrificing all his leisure hours to Union work. *The Seven Steps in the Dark* were the seven pits he worked in, as he watched his industry change from the old days of pick and shovel to total mechanisation and from private ownership to nationalisation. He is one of those once described as "the enemy within". His life shows that in fact he has been dedicated utterly to the betterment of his fellow human beings. He is a typical Trades Union man, and in many ways a typical miner.

ISBN 0 946487 21 9. Paperback £8:95p.

HIGHLAND BALLS AND VILLAGE HALLS. G.W. Lockhart.

There is no doubt about Wallace Lockhart's love of Scottish country dancing, nor of his profound knowledge of it. Reminiscence, anecdotes, social commentary and Scottish history, tartan and dress, prose and verse, the steps of the most important dances -- they are all brought together to remind, amuse and instruct the reader in all facets of Scottish country dancing. Wallace Lockhart practices what he preaches. He grew up in a house where the carpet was constantly being lifted for dancing, and the strains of country dance music have thrilled him in castle and village hall. He is the leader of the well known *Quern Players*, and he composed the dance *Eilidh MacIain,* which was the winning jig in the competition held by the Edinburgh Branch of the Royal Scottish Country Dance Society to commemorate its sixtieth anniversary.

This is a book for all who dance or who remember their dancing days. It is a book for all Scots.

ISBN 0 96487 12 X Paperback. £3:95p.

ON THE TRAIL OF ROBERT SERVICE. G.W. Lockhart

It is doubtful if any poet, except perhaps Robert Burns, has commanded such world-wide affection as Robert Service. It is doubtful if any verse has been more often recited thaan *The Shooting of Dan McGrew* and *The Cremation of Sam McGee.* Boy Scouts, learned Professors, armchair wanderers and active followers of the open road have all fallen under the spell of the man who chronicled the story of the Klondike Gold Rush. Too few know the story of the Scottish bank-clerk who became the Bard of the Yukon -- his early revolt against convention, his wandering vagabond years in the States and Canada, and his later travels in Tahiti and Russia.

This book tells the story of a man who captivated the imagination of generations, expressed the feelings and emotions of millions, and painlessly introduced countless numbers to the beauties of verse. Written with the full support of his family and containing some hitherto unpublished photographs, this book will delight Service lovers in both the Old World and the New.

ISBN 0 946487 24 3 Price: £5:95p.

Any of these books can be obtained from your bookseller, or, in case of difficulty, please send price shown, plus £1 for post and packing, to:

LUATH PRESS LTD.

BARR, AYRSHIRE. KA26 9TN